Disney's Year Book

1997

Disney's Year Book 1997

GROLIER ENTERPRISES INC.
Danbury, Connecticut

FERN L. MAMBERG   *Executive Editor*
ELIZABETH A. DeBELLA   *Designer*
HARRIETT GREYSTONE   *Production Manager*

ISBN: 0-7172-8754-8
ISSN: 0273-1274

PRINTED IN THE UNITED STATES OF AMERICA

Illustration Credits and Acknowledgments

6—(c) John Leeser; 7—(c) K. J. Fitzpatrick; (c) Ron Austing;
8—(c) Darrell Gulin/Tony Stone Images; (c) Scott Camazine/Photo Researchers, Inc.; (c) Gay Bumgarner/Tony Stone Images;
10—(c) Maslowski/Photo Researchers, Inc.; (c) Hans Reinhard/Bruce Coleman Inc.; S. Neilsen/DRK Photo; 11—(c) Wayne Lankinen/Bruce Coleman Inc.; 12-13—Artist, Vince Caputo; 26—(c) Hans Pfletschinger/ Peter Arnold; (c) Simon Trevor/Bruce Coleman Inc.; 27—(c) Michael Fogden/Bruce Coleman Inc.; (c) George Dodge/Bruce Coleman Inc.;
28—(c) David Young Wolff/Tony Stone Images; 29—Artist, Natasha Lessnik; 30—(c) Donna Day/Tony Stone Images; 31-32—Artist, Natasha Lessnik; 33—(c) Michael Freeman; (c) Jena Michel Nossant/Gamma-Liaison; 34-35—Designed and created by Jenny Tesar; 48—(c) Richard Martin/Agence Vandystadt; (c) Michael Cooper/Allsport; 49—(c) Stephane Kempinaire/Agence Vandystadt; 50 (c) Tony Duffy/NBC/Allsport;
51—(c) Mike Powell/Allsport; (c) Gary M. Prior/Allsport; 52—(c) Ross Kinnarid/Allsport; (c) Amy Sancetta/AP/Wide World; 53—(c) Doug Pensinger/Allsport; 54—Artist, Michèle A. McLean; Giraudon/Art Resource; 55-56—(c) Glenn Wolff; 57—The Natural History Museum, London; Giraudon/Art Resource; 70—(c) John Paul Endress/The Stock Market; 71—(c) Ken Cole/Animals Animals/Earth Scenes; The Granger Collection; 72—(c) Juan Silva/The Image Bank; (c) Stephen Studd/Tony Stone Images; 73—Artist, Vince Caputo; 76-77—From *Make Costumes!* (c) 1991 by F&W Publications, North Light Books, a division of F&W Publications, Inc.; 90—(c) R. Van Nostrand/Photo Researchers, Inc.;
91—(c) Tom Bledsoe/DRK Photo; 92—(c) Johnny Johnson/DRK Photo; 93—(c) Thomas Kitchin/Tom Stack & Associates; (c) Jane Burton/Bruce Coleman Inc.; 94—(c) Miriam Austerman/Animals Animals; (c) Charles Mohr/Photo Researchers, Inc.; 95—(c) Kim Taylor/Bruce Coleman Limited; (c) Kim Taylor/Bruce Coleman Inc.

Contents

IT'S FOR THE BIRDS!

Some birds will go anywhere for a handful of tasty seeds. Attracting wild birds to your backyard is easy and fun, and it helps the birds survive.

A robin hops across the lawn, looking for a tasty worm to feed her growing babies. Nearby, a sparrow takes a dust bath. A finch sits motionless on a fence, while a pair of tiny warblers rustle in the bushes. A woodpecker works its way up a tree trunk, tapping and probing with its beak in search of insects.

Would you like to see all this and more, right outside your window? All you need to do is let birds know they are welcome in your backyard. It's easy to do. Birds just need places to nest, food to eat, and water to drink.

Places to Nest. Birdhouses provide a place for birds to lay eggs and raise their young. Sometimes they are used as shelters.

Some birdhouses are very fancy, and some are just simple boxes. But every birdhouse should have a roof that slants to shed water. And the entrance should be a round hole.

Birds may not care if their birdhouse is plain or fancy. However, they care very much about the size of the house, the size of its entrance, its location, and its height above the ground. For example, sparrows nest close to the ground. But woodpeckers prefer to be high up. Wrens nest just about anywhere, but they like small houses with little entrance holes.

Helping Bluebirds

Bluebirds like to nest in tree holes. But in many places, people have cut down lots of good nesting trees. That was bad news for bluebirds. So thousands of people across America, including the kids shown here, began to build simple nest boxes for the birds.

Bluebirds moved into the boxes. They built nests and raised families. Now these pretty birds are making a comeback.

The size of a birdhouse and its entrance hole determine which birds will nest in it. Most birds like "single-family" homes. Some birds, such as purple martins, prefer "condos." And sometimes a birdhouse will double as a feeder when the nesting season is over.

Flickers want bigger houses than house finches, and house finches want bigger houses than chickadees. So you need to know what kinds of birds live nearby, and what kinds of houses would attract them.

Most birds—including finches, wrens, and chickadees—like single-family homes. But others, such as purple martins, like bird "condominiums." In this type of house, each nesting pair has its own separate "apartment." And then there are some birds that prefer nesting shelves to houses. These are just planks of wood on which the birds can build their nests.

Dining Out. Most people think of feeding birds only in winter, but many birds will come to a feeder all year long. Some birds will come every day. Others will visit just

What to Feed Your Fine-Feathered Friends

Bobwhites (quail):	cracked corn, millet, canary seed
Buntings:	grass seed, sunflower seed, thistle seed
Cardinals:	sunflower seed, cracked corn, millet
Chickadees:	sunflower seed, suet, peanut butter
Doves:	corn, millet, sunflower seed
Finches:	sunflower seed, thistle seed, millet, peanut butter
Flickers:	suet, peanut hearts
Jays:	cracked corn, sunflower seed, suet, peanut butter
Nuthatches:	sunflower seed, suet, peanut butter
Orioles:	sugar water, oranges and other fruits
Robins:	apples, sunflower seed
Sparrows:	millet, sunflower seed, canary seed, peanut butter
Towhees:	sunflower seed, cracked corn, oats, peanut hearts
Woodpeckers:	suet, sunflower seed, oranges, peanut hearts
Wrens:	peanut hearts, millet, dried fruit

occasionally or when their favorite foods are scarce. Robins, for example, feed mainly on earthworms, insects, and spiders. In fall, however, they may visit feeders stocked with fruits and seeds.

To attract a variety of birds, provide a variety of food—including fruits, suet (animal fat), and a mix of seeds. The food can be placed

To bring different birds to your backyard, offer a variety of foods. Here a wood-pecker snacks at a seed feeder. Chickadees check out a table feeder. And an oriole nibbles at a fruit feeder.

in different kinds of feeders that you can make or buy. One kind, a bird table, is just a flat wooden board set atop a post. You can put every type of food on it. Another kind of feeder holds seeds. It can be simply a long tube with a hole to eat from, or a more fancy container shaped like a birdhouse. These feeders are easy to fill and keep the seeds dry in all kinds of weather. Suet and fruit feeders can be made from plastic mesh bags, such as those used by supermarkets for onions and oranges. Just put the suet or cut fruit in the bag and hang it from a tree.

A Hummer Summer

Tiny, colorful hummingbirds, with their fast-beating wings, are fascinating to watch. They feed mainly on flower nectar. You can attract them to your backyard with a feeder filled with sugar water, like the one shown here.

You can also make one by using a hamster's water bottle. Hummingbirds are attracted to red, so place red ribbon around the drinking tube. To fill your feeder, dissolve one part sugar with two parts hot water, and then add two parts cold water.

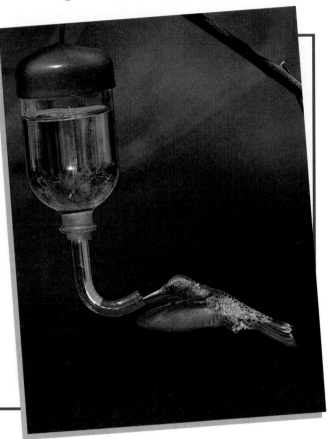

Watering Holes. Birds that never visit your birdhouses or feeders may be attracted by birdbaths, ponds, and running water. Even a shallow plastic container filled with water and a few perching stones will draw a flurry of feathery activity.

Now that your fine-feathered friends have birdhouses, food, and water, you can sit back and enjoy all the action!

Space Junk

"DON'T LITTER!" We see signs like this on streets, in parks, and in many other places *on* Earth. But there's no such sign *above* Earth. There should be. Inner space, the area from 100 to 22,000 miles above our planet, is littered with space junk. Much of this space junk, or debris, comes from the satellites, shuttles, and space stations that orbit Earth.

Nearly 8,000 large pieces of space junk are now floating around Earth. Satellites that no longer work still circle the globe. So, too, do burned-out rocket stages and pieces of exploded rockets. There are damaged solar panels and camera lens caps. In addition to these larger objects, there are millions of tiny bits of debris, like paint flakes.

This space junk isn't just messy—it's dangerous. Even a small piece could pierce a space shuttle and destroy it. And if it hit an astronaut on a space walk, it could kill him or her. In 1983, a tiny flake of paint hit the space shuttle *Challenger*. It created a ¼-inch-deep chip in one of the windows!

What are scientists doing about this? They are moving some of the old satellites so that they will enter Earth's atmosphere and burn up. They are planning to put special protective shields on spacecraft. And they are working on ways for spacecraft to dodge the debris. This will be possible because scientists know where all the big pieces of debris are. They have even made a map of all the orbiting junk.

But the best way to prevent a disaster in space is to stop leaving junk there. "DONT LITTER!" is as important a message in space as it is here on Earth.

TO THE BASEMENT... AND BEYOND!

"ROOAAARRR!" Rex hollered at the top of his lungs when he spotted Woody walking by. He jumped out from under Andy's bed and blocked the cowboy's path. "Run for your life! Tremble in fear! The mighty Tyrannosaurus Rex is here!" shouted the toy dinosaur.

Woody just doubled over in laughter. "Give it up, pardner," he chuckled. "The dust bunnies under the bed could have bushwhacked me better than you."

Rex was disappointed. He always tried really hard to act like his ferocious dinosaur namesake. He didn't care for Woody's teasing one bit. I'll show him, the miffed dinosaur thought.

14

That night, long after Andy had fallen asleep, Rex looked up "Tyrannosaurus Rex" in the boy's encyclopedia. He read the book carefully, trying to learn how the terrible Thunder Lizard scared all the other dinosaurs.

Rex closed the book, his plastic heart swelling with pride. His ancestors were a fearsome bunch, indeed! The inspired dinosaur swaggered out of Andy's bedroom, ready for action.

Woody and Buzz Lightyear saw Rex leave. Their curiosity got the better of them, and they trailed Rex into the hallway, where the dinosaur used his tiny arms to hoist himself into the laundry chute at the end of the hall.

"You'd better keep away from there," warned Woody. "That hole leads straight to the basement."

But Rex wouldn't listen. "I looked up 'Tyrannosaurus Rex' in Andy's encyclopedia. Now I know how they scared all the other dinosaurs," he bragged. "All I have to do is hide in this. . . cave. Then I can ambush anybody who's foolish enough to walk by me."

Of course, Rex only surprised himself when he stepped inside the laundry chute and found that it didn't have a floor. Rex dropped down the chute like a stone!

Woody felt responsible. After all, he had sort of forced Rex to prove himself fearsome. Rex would be scared all alone down there in the basement. "I'm going after the big guy!" he said.

Buzz held up his hand. "I'd think twice about a rescue mission, if I were you, Sheriff. Rex has been whisked into another dimension."

"What are you talking about?" asked Woody.

Buzz paced back and forth. He explained how he had "put two and two together" once he saw how quickly Rex had disappeared. Obviously, their bulky buddy had been "transported" at "light speed" into the domain of Buzz's

archenemy—the evil emperor Zurg. "Face it, Woody," Buzz concluded. "Rex has entered. . .the ZURG ZONE!"

Woody rolled his eyes. He tried his best to talk Buzz out of this silly theory, but the space ranger stubbornly clung to it. Finally, Woody threw up his arms in frustration. . .and tipped into the laundry chute faster than Andy's Etch-A-Sketch toy could draw.

Buzz grabbed Woody's leg to try to stop him, but the cowboy's weight ended up pulling the astronaut along for the ride.

A laundry basket filled with bed sheets broke their wild fall. Woody and Buzz timidly peeked over the rim. The gloomy basement was crowded with stuff. They couldn't see Rex anywhere. Then they spied several large footprints on the dusty floor. But Woody and Buzz didn't recognize them as their dinosaur friend's tracks.

"These are Galactic Gulpdersnatch tracks," Buzz announced. "Only a diabolical fiend like Emperor Zurg would dare to disobey space monster leash laws and let one run wild in. . .the ZURG ZONE!"

18

Woody clapped a hand over Buzz's mouth. He didn't believe in Gulpdersnatches, but he did hear a strange, rustling sound.

Rex was frantically trying to wriggle under some old newspapers. The poor dinosaur had been badly frightened by the commotion his friends had made when they tumbled down the laundry chute after him.

"This place gives me the heeby-jeebies!" Rex whimpered to himself. "I just know it's haunted!"

The very idea of ghosts was enough to send Rex on the run once more. He ran into a lamp, which toppled over and hit the back of an old dressmaker's dummy. Rex ran one way and the dummy rolled the other, skidding across the floor in the direction of Woody and Buzz.

Buzz knocked the cowboy out of the dummy's path as

it loomed at them in the darkness. "Run for your life!" he yelled. "It's the Galactic Gulpdersnatch!" In the gloom, the dummy really did look like a monster. Woody and Buzz leaped for cover under some burlap sacks.

At that moment, Rex ran by and gaped at the wriggling sacks. "Ghosts!" he screamed.

Woody untangled his head from the pile of cloth. "Rex!" he shouted. But it was too dark for the dinosaur to see him.

"Aaahh! The ghost knows my name!" Rex gasped. The terrified Tyrannosaur veered away and galloped deeper into the basement.

Woody slumped over. "This is gonna be one mighty long night!"

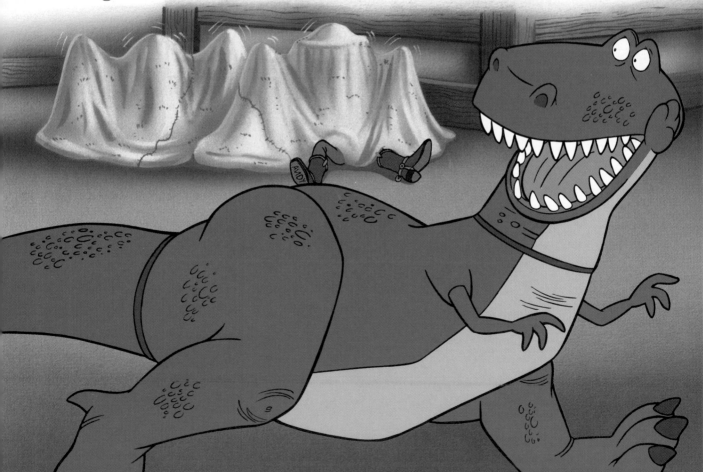

Indeed, hours passed as Woody and Buzz walked in circles in the dark basement, trying to catch up with Rex—without any luck. Every time they heard the pitter-patter CRASH! of Rex's clumsy feet, Buzz and Woody changed direction to follow the sound, only to find that Rex had eluded them once more.

By this time, Rex had worked himself into a frenzy trying to stay one step ahead of the "ghost" he was sure was hot on his trail. The tired beast crawled into an overturned storage box. "I'm such a coward," he whined. "Even the picture of my own kind in Andy's encyclopedia scared me. I'll never be a good T. Rex."

Nearby, Buzz had halted in front of a familiar object loaded with bed sheets. Woody stumbled into him.

"Aha! Emperor Zurg's sleeping chamber," Buzz declared, patting the soft folded sheets. "Don't ask me how, but we've managed to sneak past his superior forces, right into his lair."

"Oh, for Pete's sake! It's just the laundry basket," Woody exclaimed. "We've been going around in cir—"

Woody was interrupted by another mysterious rustling. All of a sudden, a large, nasty rat lunged at the two toys, its eyes glowing red with hunger. Buzz struck a heroic pose and flashed his laser wrist beam. The rat, however, was unimpressed, and the angry animal forced Buzz and Woody up against the laundry basket.

"We're trapped, Sheriff!" shouted Buzz. "Trapped like rats by yet another Gulpdersnatch in. . .the ZURG ZONE!"

"Buzz, that is a. . .oh, never mind," the cowboy sputtered. Both Woody and Buzz began shouting for help.

The minute Rex heard his friends' voices, he forgot his own fear. Mustering his courage, he dashed out to help them. Rex leaped in front of the rat and opened his toothy mouth wide. Then he let loose the loudest, most awesome Thunder Lizard "ROOOAAARRR!" of his life!

The surprised rat jumped in the air and scampered off, yelling "Squeak! Squeak! Squeak!"

Woody and Buzz danced around
Rex, cheering. Even Rex was
amazed by his new-found ferocity.
"Well, what do you know! I finally got in touch with my inner
predator," he said. He waved his tiny arms in triumphant play-
attack.

Just then, the basement door creaked open and morning
sunshine poured through. The sight of his own "attacking"
shadow startled Rex, and he fainted dead away.

Woody looked up as a boy's figure stepped into the doorway.
"It's Andy!" he cried.

"He braved the ZURG ZONE—just to save us," added a
touched Buzz.

Woody and Buzz dropped to the floor beside Rex. Andy, who had really braved the basement to get some clean playclothes, was puzzled to see his toys lying near the laundry basket. He couldn't remember leaving them there at all.

Andy gathered Rex, Buzz, and Woody up in his arms and hugged them tight. "I'm so glad you guys are here," he whispered to Woody. "The basement isn't half as creepy with you along."

Woody knew he could never break the rules and answer Andy. Still, a secret smile of agreement spread across his cowboy face.

The metallic colors of the **leaf beetle** make it look like a living gem. As their name suggests, leaf beetles feed mostly on plant leaves. Many of them, such as the Colorado potato beetle and the spotted cucumber beetle, cause a lot of damage by eating crops.

The huge **Goliath beetle** of Africa is one of the largest flying insects in the world. It may be 5 inches long. The male has curved "horns" that grow on its head. Despite their size and the fact that they make a loud, whirring noise when they fly, Goliath beetles are quite harmless.

All About BEETLES

Have you ever seen a firefly blink its way across the sky? Or watched a polka-dotted ladybug fly by? Then you have met two of the world's 300,000 kinds of beetles! Beetles are a varied bunch of bugs. Their bodies are decorated with bright colors and patterns. Their shapes range from long and slender to round, and

The **snout beetle** is named for its long, slender snout, or beak. Its mouthparts, on the tip of the snout, are used for eating leaves, seeds, and fruits. Many snout beetles destroy crops and stored grains. If disturbed, a snout beetle may "play possum," or pretend that it is dead.

The body of the **tortoise beetle** is shaped somewhat like the body of a turtle or tortoise. But this beetle acts more like a chameleon—it can change its color to better blend with its surroundings. The target tortoise beetle shown here is named for the bull's-eye target on its back.

from boxlike to flat and thin. There are giraffe beetles with long "necks." And there are diving beetles with fringed hind legs for swimming. Despite these differences, all beetles have something no other insects have—two sets of wings. Thick, leathery front wings cover the beetle's body. They act as shields for the back wings, which are used for flying. Because of these shields, beetles are called the "armored tanks" of the insect world.

YOUR SCENT-SATIONAL SENSE OF SMELL

What smell do you like best? The scent of flowers from a garden? A whiff of fresh-baked apple pie? Grass that's just been mowed? Whatever it is, when you smell it, you feel good all over. What smell do you like least? Skunk? Six-day-old garbage? Your gym sneakers? Phew! How do those smells make you feel?

In recent years, scientists have learned a lot about our sense of smell. And they have learned that what we smell seems to be linked to our feelings. As a result, people are using scents in new ways.

One of the newest ways to use scent is called "aromatherapy." Aromatherapy is based on the idea that smells affect the way you feel. A whiff of the right scent, the theory goes, can help you handle life's little problems. Are you so excited about an upcoming party that you have trouble sleeping? Then the calming scent of lavender may help you drift off. Are you stressed out because of a difficult school assignment? Try vanilla, spiced apple, or chamomile scents to help you relax. Feeling dull and draggy? Pep up with a whiff of peppermint or lemon. The point is to let your nose come to your rescue!

The idea of aromatherapy isn't new. The ancient Egyptians believed in the power of perfume.

Your Nose Knows!

People have five sense organs. We feel with our skin, see with our eyes, hear with our ears, taste with our tongues, and smell with our noses. These organs allow us to know what's going on in the world around us.

When you smell something, you are actually detecting chemicals that are given off by an object such as a flower. The air carries these chemicals into your nose. Nerve cells in your nose send a message to your brain. Your brain recognizes the scent. You think "flower"—and you feel happy!

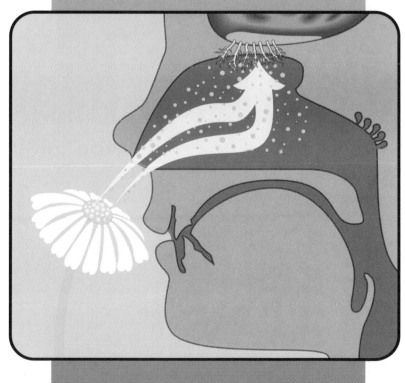

They had specific scents for nearly everything they did—including going into battle. Scents have long been part of medical treatment in India and the Middle East. Even in the West, many folk remedies relied on smell. And recent studies have shown that there's plenty of truth behind the idea that scents can help people feel better.

Today, many people buy scented products to add good smells to the air. Some people like to use bowls of potpourri—a mixture of dried flowers, herbs, and spices. Others use sweet-smelling sprays, scented candles, and fragrant oils. In Japan, some people use special alarm clocks that send out a mist of wake-up aroma.

Manufacturers have long added scents to products to help them sell. Now, however,

These shelves are filled with sweet-smelling oils and fragrant herbs and spices.

Test Your Nose

The human nose is capable of identifying thousands of smells. But in reality, most of us can't pick out more than a few hundred. How much does *your* nose know? Try this test with a friend.

1. Put on a blindfold.

2. Ask your friend to hold different things under your nose. Try foods, such as cheese, onions, and fruits. Or try products such as shampoo, soap, and toothpaste. Don't use household cleaning products or other harsh chemicals—some produce harmful fumes.

3. How many smells can you identify? Most people can pick out about seven out of every ten smells. If you do better, you may have a great nose!

Test Your Taste

Do you know that most flavors in food are really aromas? When you lift food to your mouth, its odor molecules enter your nose. Or they enter at the back of your mouth, where nasal passages connect with the throat. You can test this by eating four or five different flavors of jelly beans.

1. Put on a blindfold.

2. Pinch your nose firmly closed with your fingers.

3. Ask your friend to hand you different flavored jelly beans. Try to guess the flavors as you eat them.

4. Keep the blindfold on, but stop pinching your nose. Try the test again. Is it easier to guess the different flavors?

fragrance is being used not just in products but in the stores where they are sold. The next time you go to a mall, take a good sniff as you walk in the door of each store you visit. Chances are that you will smell enticing aromas at several of them. These good smells are one way the stores say "come on in!"

31

How are perfumes and room scents created? Perfumes are usually made from natural scents—mainly fragrant oils that are extracted from flowers and other plants. Not all plants contain these oils, and perfume makers search the world to find the most fragrant plants.

The flowers, or whatever parts of the plant will yield scent, are picked by hand in early morning. This is when they are covered with dew, and their aromas are fresh and strong. Next,

A Blast from the Past!

Just the whiff of an aroma can bring back memories of the past. You recall where you were and what you were doing the first time you smelled that scent. But one study found that age makes a difference when it comes to which smells are linked to childhood memories. People born before 1930 reacted to the scents of baking bread, cinnamon, burning leaves, cut grass, honeysuckle, pine, and other natural aromas. Those born after 1930 grew nostalgic when they smelled engine fuel, nail polish, scented felt-tip markers, and other chemical scents.

Young workers in Bulgaria harvest rose petals for perfume-making (above). The petals are crushed and then distilled (right) to produce rose oil. It takes 4,000 pounds of rose petals to produce just a pound of rose oil!

they are crushed and processed into scented oils. The oils are then blended with other fragrant chemicals and alcohol to make perfumes and other fragrances. Experts known as "noses" do the blending. "Noses" can recognize some 1,500 aromas. The very best "noses" can identify twice as many as that.

Some experts say that nothing smells as good as the scent of a real flower. But scientists can now make artificial ingredients that mimic the natural aromas. That means there are even more fabulous ways to scent your world and give your spirits a lift!

NIFTY
NOTEBOOKS

Would you like to have a one-of-a-kind notebook for school or home? You can make one by turning a plain plastic binder or a hardcover notebook into a piece of art. It's easy to do, and it's lots of fun.

Six different designs are shown here. They are made with pieces of felt and fabric, fabric paints, stickers, ribbon, and wiggle eyes. You can also use buttons, bows, pompoms, sequins, glitter, and many other materials.

Make your own designs, too. Do you love sports? Paint balls and bats on a cover. Which rock and movie stars do you like best? Put their pictures on your cover. You can even put a mini-notepad into your design to help you remember things. Just use your imagination, and you'll have a nifty notebook of your own.

A Bride For Prince Mickey

"My son, 'tis time for you to marry," said the King.

Prince Mickey sighed. Choosing a bride was not an easy task.

"Would you like us to give a ball, Mickey? Your father and I know how much you love to dance. We could invite princesses from throughout the land," suggested the Queen.

"Call me old-fashioned," added the King, "but I do love going to a ball. Besides, Mickey, it's tradition."

Prince Mickey hugged his mother. "No, thanks," he said. "I know you and Father met at a ball, and I always enjoy your glass-slipper story. But I don't think I will find *my* princess at a ball."

The King and Queen exchanged a knowing look. They were still as much in love as on that fateful midnight when she ran off, leaving only a glass slipper. . .but that's another story.

Prince Mickey wanted no ordinary bride. "I want a princess who is good and kind, and cares about her subjects, and loves music and dancing. She must be clever and brave and. . ." Mickey stopped. The King and Queen were laughing. "What's so funny?"

"My son, we want your princess to be all those things and more. But how will you find such a royal spouse?" the King asked.

The Queen said, "Do you have a plan?"

"Yes," Mickey said, "I do."

In a few days, Prince Mickey was ready to put his plan into action. Visits were arranged to all the kingdoms with suitable princesses. Mickey's party included three special "gifts" for the

princesses. They were his personal physician, Doctor Sophie; Maestro Perlie, the great violinist; and Master Tyler, the brilliant architect and builder. Each princess would have the use of their services for the length of Mickey's visit. Prince Mickey told his parents, "I'm sure that the way each princess uses my unusual gifts will reveal her true character." And so Mickey and his party set off.

The first stop on Prince Mickey's tour was to see Princess Bella. Bella's parents greeted Prince Mickey with a long, lavish luncheon that consisted of fifteen courses. And each dish was accompanied by a different form of entertainment. Prince Mickey and Princess Bella were amused by jugglers juggling pineapples, chairs, and even pigs. They saw magicians pull dragons out of hats. And they watched singers and dancers of all shapes and sizes. But at last they were alone.

She is very beautiful, thought Mickey, smiling at the lovely princess. Princess Bella was quite pretty

and she knew it.
Unfortunately, she was
also quite vain. She spent
most of her time admiring
herself in the mirror, trying on
her vast collection of jewels, and changing her gowns. Princess
Bella had hundreds of gowns, and each one had a special pair of
shoes to go with it.

In a sweet voice, the Princess asked coyly, "What did you
bring me, Prince Mickey?"

Prince Mickey proudly introduced his "gifts": Doctor Sophie,
Maestro Perlie, and Master Tyler.

Princess Bella was stunned. "What! No jewels? No gowns?
No shoes? No, thanks!" she cried.

Prince Mickey and his party left that same afternoon.

Next on Mickey's list was Princess Mimi. Unlike Princess

40

Bella, Princess Mimi was truly delighted with Mickey's "gifts." But before Mickey could say, "What a lovely palace you have here," Princess Mimi whisked away Doctor Sophie, Maestro Perlie, and Master Tyler.

For days, Prince Mickey didn't see his "gifts" and only caught glimpses of Mimi in passing. The rest of the royal family took turns entertaining him. The King and Mickey went fishing. The Queen and Mickey rode all the horses in the royal stables. The Duke and Mickey toured surrounding villages.

When Mickey finally did see Doctor Sophie, he asked, "How is Princess Mimi?"

"Oh!" the doctor exclaimed. "Every bitty bump, every small scratch and scrape! That girl is one royal pain!"

Just then, a page ran up to them. "Come quickly, Doctor. The Princess needs you." Doctor Sophie shrugged her shoulders and followed the page.

Later that day, Mickey found Maestro Perlie in the kitchen, soaking his hands in ice water. "What is the matter with your hands, Perlie?"

Perlie showed Mickey his bruised and swollen fingers. "She would not let me stop to rest! She's ruined my hands!"

Horrified, Mickey assured him, "You will not play another note on your violin for Princess Mimi!"

In the princess's private garden, Prince Mickey discovered Master Tyler putting the finishing touches on a miniature castle. "What is this for?" Mickey asked.

"It is for Her Highness to play in," the builder replied.

What a vain, uncaring, insensitive person she is, thought Prince Mickey.

"It is time for us to leave," he told Master Tyler.

Prince Mickey and his party went to visit the third kingdom

on his list, the home of Princess Minnie. Just as Mickey and his party entered the throne room, the Prince was practically knocked over by a villager rushing in to see the King. "Where have you been?" the King demanded angrily.

"Sire!" cried the villager. "There's been an accident! Hurry!"

A roof had collapsed in the town square. Prince Mickey and his party rushed out with the others. Racing to the accident, the villager asked who he and the others were. Prince Mickey explained, "I am Prince Mickey. Doctor Sophie, Perlie the musician, and Tyler the builder are my gifts to the Princess."

Before Mickey could ask his own questions, the villager said, "Sire and Prince Mickey, help those men move the heavy beams. Doctor Sophie, Maestro Perlie, Master Tyler, you come with me."

44

Thanks to quick thinking and cooperation, no one was badly hurt. But there was much work to be done. The villager took Doctor Sophie to the first-aid station set up near the village fountain. Maestro Perlie joined those who were trying to calm and entertain the crying children. Master Tyler met with the town planners to draw up designs for a new village square.

Back in the palace, Prince Mickey said, "What a remarkable subject, Your Majesty! Are all your people so clever and brave as that peasant villager?"

The King muttered, "That was no peasant, that was . . ." But

then he decided it was better to wait. Instead, he graciously thanked Prince Mickey and the others for their help.

Prince Mickey bowed and replied, "We are glad to have been of service, Your Majesty. Now, when shall I meet Princess Minnie?"

"You already have," said a familiar voice.

"Princess? Peasant?" Mickey stared in disbelief. A washed and begowned peasant turned out to be Princess Minnie herself.

Princess Minnie laughed. "Yes, *this* is me and *that* was me."

The King explained, "Princess Minnie often dresses as one of her subjects to spend some time among the common people."

" 'Tis the best training for a future queen. And the only way to know your subjects' hearts," she added modestly.

Mickey's own heart skipped a beat. "You have already won mine," he said, kissing her hand.

Princess Minnie was indeed the princess of his dreams: good, kind, intelligent, and brave. But did she love music and dancing?

To celebrate the engagement of their children, the kings and queens of both kingdoms gave a grand ball. Prince Mickey and Princess Minnie danced every dance together, as if they had been dancing together their whole lives.

It was a wonderful ball. It was a beautiful ball. Prince Mickey's mother wiped a tear from her eye as she leaned her head on the King's shoulder.

"Yes, my dear. I know," he said softly. "This ball is almost as wonderful as the one you ran from when the clock struck midnight."

But that's another story.

AN OLYMPIC CELEBRATION

The 26th Summer Olympic Games were held in Atlanta, Georgia, from July 19 through August 4, 1996. It was the biggest sports event the world had ever seen. The Games were special for another reason, too. They marked the 100th anniversary of the modern Olympic Games.

The Olympic Games had been held in ancient Greece for more than 1,100 years—until the Roman emperor banned them in 394. More than 1,500 years

At the spectacular opening ceremonies, Muhammad Ali lights the Olympic flame. The American boxer had won a gold medal at the 1960 Olympics.

later they were brought back to life. The first modern Olympic Games were held in Athens, Greece, in 1896.

The Olympics have come a long way in the 100 years since the first modern Games were played. At the 1896 Games, 311 athletes from 13 countries competed in 9 sports. At the 1996 Games, some 10,000 athletes from 197 countries competed in 33 sports! There was another big difference. There were no women athletes at the 1896 Games—they didn't compete until 1900. At the 1996 Games, there were nearly 4,000 women athletes.

A record number of medals—842—were given out at the Summer Games. United States athletes won the most medals. They collected a total of 101, including 44 gold.

The official mascot of the 1996 Summer Olympic Games was a blue-bodied, red-sneakered cartoon character. At first, he was called Whatizit. But a panel of kids came up with a better name—Izzy.

The exciting performances of a few of the Olympic winners are described here.

Amanda Borden, Dominique Dawes, Amy Chow, Jaycie Phelps, Dominique Moceanu, Kerri Strug, and Shannon Miller, U.S.—team gymnastics.

For the first time ever, seven young athletes from the United States won the team competition in women's gymnastics. Their efforts in the floor exercise and on the balance beam, vault, and parallel bars placed them ahead of the talented Russian and Romanian teams. This earned them gold medals—and the nickname "The Magnificent Seven." One of the heroes of the American team was Kerri Strug (above, second from right). Despite a painfully sprained left ankle, she made an outstanding second vault.

American Carl Lewis did something that no other track star had ever done. He soared to a fourth consecutive Olympic gold medal in the long jump. And that medal gave him something that only three other Olympians have—a total of nine gold medals.

"I want to make history," said U.S. sprinter Michael Johnson. And he did! Running in his golden track shoes, he became the first

Right: Carl Lewis, U.S.—long jump.
Below: Michael Johnson, U.S.—
200-meter and 400-meter races.

man to win the gold medal in both the 400-meter run and 200-meter dash.

Amy Van Dyken became America's new sweetheart of swimming. She won gold medals in the 100-meter butterfly and the 50-meter

freestyle. And she was a member of the gold-medal-winning 400-meter freestyle and 400-meter medley teams. This made her the first U.S. woman to win four gold medals in the same Olympics.

Fu Mingxia, China—two gold medals in diving.

At the 1992 Summer Olympics, when she was only 13 years old, China's Fu Mingxia won the gold medal in women's platform diving. At the 1996 Games, at age 17, she was even better. She took the gold medals in both platform diving and springboard diving.

New sports are often added to the Olympic Games. Beach volleyball was one of the new sports added in 1996. The exciting battles between the two-member teams made this sport one of the most popular events at the Olympics. The Brazilian team won the women's

Karch Kiraly, U.S.—beach volleyball. His gold-medal-winning partner was Kent Steffes.

competition, and the American team won the men's. Karch Kiraly of the men's team had previously won gold medals in indoor volleyball at the 1984 and 1988 Olympics.

❊LEGEND OF THE UNICORN❊

There are in India certain wild animals that are as large as horses and even larger. Their bodies are white, their heads dark red, and their eyes dark blue. They have a horn in the middle of their forehead.

This is how one writer described unicorns 2,300 years ago. At that time, and for hundreds of years after, there were reports about these animals all over the world. But no one actually ever saw a unicorn— because there were never any to see. The unicorn is a legendary, or imaginary, animal.

The unicorn is named for the single horn that grows from its forehead. (*Unicorn* comes from Latin words that mean "one" and "horn.") Apart from the horn, however, descriptions of unicorns varied widely. The people of ancient China thought it was a shy and gentle animal. They said it had the body of a deer, the feet of a horse, and the tail of an ox. Its coat was splashed with red, yellow, blue, black, and white markings. And its horn was short and blunt. In ancient Persia and India, the unicorn was said to have the body of a horse, the head of a stag, the feet of an elephant, and the tail of a boar. Its horn was three feet long.

The picture most people have of the unicorn comes from

How to Catch a Unicorn

Unicorns were thought to be so fast and so smart that it was just about impossible to catch one alive. But medieval writings describe some ways to do it—usually by trickery.

One way to catch a unicorn required a great deal of courage. Unicorn hunters were told to chase and annoy the animal until it was angry enough to attack them. Then one hunter was to stand in front of a tree as the animal charged directly at him. At the last minute, the hunter would leap aside. The unicorn's horn would go into the tree instead of the hunter, and the animal would be stuck fast.

medieval Europe, between the years 500 and 1500. The unicorn of that time was thought to be a graceful creature that looked partly like a horse and partly like a stag. Its pointed horn was long, straight, and usually spiral-shaped. This unicorn was a fierce fighter, yet it could also be quite gentle.

But if unicorns never existed, where did all the stories about them come from? They probably began with explorers who saw real but unfamiliar animals with horns. Perhaps they saw the oryx (an Arabian antelope) or the rhinoceros. Long ago, most people didn't travel far. And they were quite willing to believe that strange creatures lived just over the horizon. So for centuries, no one questioned whether unicorns were real.

Also, no one questioned the claims that unicorn horns had magical powers. Kings, queens, and nobles bought unicorn horns, believing that the horn could destroy poisons in food and drink. And some people thought that unicorn powder, made by crushing and grinding

There have been many different descriptions of the legendary unicorn. Perhaps they were based on the oryx, or other long-horned animals that actually existed.

Unicorns of the Sea

Long ago, European kings and queens treasured their unicorn horns. These long twisting horns were real enough, but they didn't come from unicorns. Many were the tusks of the male narwhal, an odd little whale that lives in Arctic waters and is often called the "unicorn of the sea." The tusk is actually an enlarged tooth that can grow up to 10 feet.

unicorn horn, could cure illnesses. But since unicorns weren't real, what were these people actually buying? Unicorn horns were usually rhinoceros horns or the tusks of narwhals, small whales. Unicorn powder was the crushed bones of any animal.

We know now that unicorns are imaginary. Yet stories about them are still popular. In today's tales, unicorns combine the best features of the unicorns of ancient and medieval legends. They are delicate, graceful, gentle, and pure. It's nice to think that such animals might exist—if not on Earth, then forever in legend.

Quasimodo–The Kid Sitter

"Quasimodo, would you take care of Djali for me today?" Esmeralda asked one morning. "Phoebus and I have to go somewhere."

"Djali and I could come with you," Quasimodo replied, looking up from a figure he was carving. "It would be fun."

"We need to run this errand alone," Esmeralda answered. "Please help me. I'll leave some hay for Djali to eat. I'm sure he won't be any trouble."

"All right," Quasimodo agreed, although he was disappointed.

Djali didn't want to be left behind. When Esmeralda started to leave, he grabbed her skirt in his mouth and tugged.

"Now Djali—behave," Esmeralda said. She freed her skirt
and left. Djali was mad. He kicked his heels against the door
and bleated. He ran outside onto the parapet and butted his
head against the stone gargoyles who were Quasimodo's
friends. Then he ran off again.

"Quasimodo, this kid needs discipline," Hugo and Victor
complained.

"Let me at him. I'll cool his heels," said Laverne.

"I'm sorry," Quasimodo apologized. "I'll take him into my
workroom so he won't bother you again."

Quasimodo led Djali into his workroom. "Please behave,
Djali," he pleaded.

"Baah, baah, baah," Djali answered sadly.

"I know you wanted to go with Esmeralda and Phoebus," Quasimodo answered. "So did I. But we can have a nice time together. Wait here, and I'll bring you some hay to eat." And Quasimodo hurried off to get the hay.

While he was gone, Djali looked around the workroom. It was filled with interesting things that Quasimodo had made. On a long wooden table were tiny figures and houses that Quasimodo had carved and brightly painted. Djali didn't know what they were. But they looked very tasty.

Crunch! Djali chomped a figure of a man in a

bright yellow hat. *Chomp!* He chewed a plump lady in a green gown. *Blecch!* The figures sure looked a lot better than they tasted.

Then Djali noticed a beautiful mobile hanging above the table. It was made of many bits of glass that sparkled in the light coming through the window. The deep purple and bright red glass pieces reminded Djali of grapes and apples—the fruits he loved best!

With a happy bleat, Djali leaped onto the table. He stood on his hind legs and pawed at the mobile with his forelegs, making it swing close enough to grab with his mouth.

Just then, Quasimodo returned with his arms full of hay. "Djali, what are you doing!" He exclaimed. "Get down right now!"

Startled, Djali turned and jumped, but his forelegs got tangled in the mobile strings. Crash! Djali fell to the floor, pulling the mobile down with him. Tangled in the mobile strings, Djali skittered and scampered around the room, knocking bits of glass, hay, and wooden figures helter skelter.

Finally, Quasimodo caught Djali and untangled the mobile.

"Djali, what am I going to do with you?" Quasimodo sighed. "I have to clean up this mess. But I'm afraid you'll get into more trouble while I work."

Quasimodo had an idea. He found a long piece of rope and tied it to Djali's collar. He led the little goat out to the parapet and tied the other end of the rope to Laverne. Then he put a pile of hay down for Djali to eat.

"Get that goat away from me," Laverne hissed at Quasimodo.

Djali thought he heard something. He looked around quickly. Laverne snapped her mouth shut just in time.

"It's only for a few minutes, Laverne," Quasimodo answered. "I'll be right back."

With a puzzled frown, Djali glanced around to see who Quasimodo was talking to. He stared at Laverne suspiciously. Laverne stared back and held still. Djali blinked, shook his head, and began to eat his hay.

As soon as Djali wasn't looking, Laverne slipped the rope off and gave him a swift little push. Startled, Djali jumped away. Then, with a happy bleat, he realized that the rope was loose! He was free!

Skipping and jumping, Djali ran around and around the parapet. Then he climbed on Laverne's head and leaped up onto the edge of the cathedral roof. Climbing looked like fun. So up Djali went.

As Djali started to climb, Quasimodo came out. "I'm finished cleaning up," Quasimodo called to Djali. "I'm sorry I—" Quasimodo stopped. He looked around. Djali was nowhere to be seen.

"Djali! Djali, where are you?"
Quasimodo called. He rushed to
the edge of the parapet and looked
down. He was frightened. What if Djali
had fallen?

Then Quasimodo heard a mischievous bleat from the rooftop.
There was Djali, peeking around a spire.

"Djali, come down!" Quasimodo shouted. "You'll fall!"

But Djali just bleated and climbed higher.

Quasimodo started to climb after the little goat. Up and up
he went, higher and higher. But each time he got close to Djali,
the little goat scampered out of reach.

At last Djali climbed to the very top of the cathedral. Now
there was nowhere else to go. Djali looked down. The ground

was very far away. A strong wind was blowing around the spires and towers. It felt to Djali as if the wind wanted to push him off. Suddenly, climbing wasn't fun anymore. He was afraid.

"Djali, come back down," Quasimodo pleaded. But Djali was too frightened to move. His feet felt frozen in place. All he could do was stand and cry.

Quasimodo finally reached him. "It's all right, Djali," he said gently. "I'm here to help you." He lifted the frightened goat onto his shoulders and began climbing down.

From far below, Quasimodo heard someone calling his name. He looked down and saw Esmeralda and Phoebus racing up the cathedral steps, shouting and waving. Just then, Quasimodo's

foot slipped. With a
loud cry, he and Djali
slid down the roof and
tumbled over the parapet.

"Help!" Quasimodo shouted as he
and Djali flew past the gargoyles. Laverne saw the end of
Djali's rope go slithering past her base. Instantly, she jumped
on it, then froze in place before anyone could see her move.

With a jerk, the rope tightened and held. For a second, Djali
and Quasimodo dangled in the air. Swiftly, Quasimodo reached
up and grabbed the rope just above Djali's collar. Hanging by
one hand, he lifted Djali back onto his shoulders. Then, hand
over hand, Quasimodo pulled himself and Djali up the rope to
the parapet.

Esmeralda and Phoebus were waiting to pull Quasimodo and Djali to safety. For a long time, the friends laughed and cried and hugged each other without speaking.

At last, Esmeralda wiped her eyes. "Oh dear! I was so upset, I almost forgot," she exclaimed. "Come down to the street, Quasimodo. Phoebus and I have a surprise for you."

There in the town square stood a beautiful little wood cart. While Quasimodo gazed at the cart, Esmeralda slipped a red leather harness with bells over Djali's head.

"Our errand today was to get this cart for you," Esmeralda explained. "That's why I asked you to take care of Djali. We wanted the cart and harness to be a surprise for you both. Now you can go for rides in the country with us. And Djali will pull you wherever you want to go.

"I hope this cart makes up for all the trouble Djali caused you today," Esmeralda continued. For a moment, Quasimodo was too surprised and happy to answer. He simply watched Djali dancing along to the jingle of his harness bells.

"Why, Esmeralda," Quasimodo answered, grinning. "Taking care of Djali was as easy as falling off a log—or in this case, the roof!"

CRAZY FOR CHOCOLATE

Chocolate. Sweet, delicious chocolate. Nothing tastes quite so yummy as this treat made from the beans of the cacao tree. No wonder, then, that chocolate has been called the "food of the gods."

What chocolate treat do *you* like best? Chocolate ice cream? Chocolate chip cookies? Chocolate fudge? A cup of cocoa? If your answer is a chocolate drink, then you love something that's been around for hundreds of years. Long before Christopher Columbus sailed to the New World, the Aztecs of Mexico brewed a drink from the beans of the cacao tree. It wasn't sweet like the hot cocoa we drink today. In fact, it was cold and bitter. But the Aztec king drank as many as 50 cups a day!

Hernando Cortes, the Spanish explorer who conquered the Aztecs in the 1500s, believed that the drink had special powers and could make people stronger. So he sent the wonderful cacao beans back to Spain. The Spanish added sugar, vanilla, and cinnamon to the liquid to make it sweeter and tastier, and everyone loved it. By the end of the 1600s, people all over Europe were drinking chocolate. The custom of drinking chocolate then went back across the Atlantic to North America. Now, however, people were not only drinking chocolate, they were also nibbling on it. These first chocolate bars were just tablets of coarse-ground chocolate and sugar. But in the 1800s, factories began to make smooth, creamy eating chocolate and chocolate syrups. Today chocolate-making is a very big industry.

Above: Cacao beans form inside big oval pods. Right: In this 16th-century print, an Aztec worker grinds cacao beans for use in a drink.

cacuuate

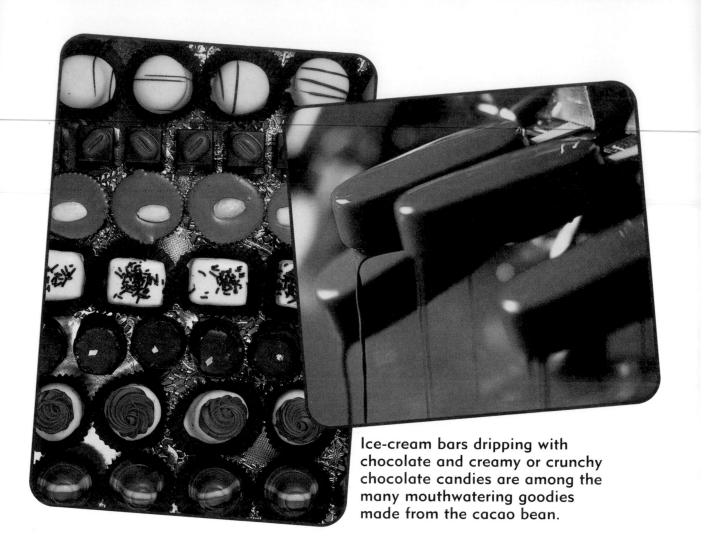

Ice-cream bars dripping with chocolate and creamy or crunchy chocolate candies are among the many mouthwatering goodies made from the cacao bean.

How is chocolate made? The process starts with the beans. They form inside large oval pods that grow on the trunk and branches of the cacao tree. Workers harvest the pods and scoop out the beans. The beans are left to ferment for a few days, and then they are dried and shipped off to the chocolate factory. At the factory, the beans are cleaned, roasted, and shelled. The soft centers are crushed to make a dark paste known as chocolate liquor. Despite its name, chocolate liquor has no alcohol. But it is more than half fat, and this fat is called cocoa butter.

To make powdered cocoa, most of the cocoa butter is pressed out of the chocolate liquor. What's left of the chocolate liquor is then ground and sifted. To make chocolate bars, the chocolate liquor is blended with extra cocoa butter, sugar, vanilla, and sometimes powdered milk. The chocolate is then blended in a huge tub for hours or even days—which gives the chocolate its silky texture. After this step, the chocolate is formed into bars and other shapes.

In North America, the average person eats about 10 pounds of chocolate every year. But the Swiss people average more than 20 pounds a year! They must truly believe that chocolate is the "food of the gods."

Chocolate Chips

- The botanical name of the cacao tree is *theobroma cacao. Theobroma* comes from Greek words that mean "food of the gods."
- It takes 400 cacao beans to make a pound of chocolate.
- Who says money doesn't grow on trees? The Aztecs used cacao beans as currency. A rabbit cost four beans.
- The fictional detective Sherlock Holmes drank hot chocolate for breakfast.
- In the early 1800s, American candy maker Milton Hershey created a chocolate bar that wouldn't melt in tropical heat. His Hershey bars became part of the standard food for U.S. troops.
- The largest chocolate egg in the world weighed 5,000 pounds and was almost 18 feet tall.

HOORAY FOR LEAP YEAR!

Why was 1996 a special year? Because it was a Leap Year! What's so special about that? Well, Leap Year happens only once every four years. And it has 366 days instead of the usual 365. The extra day is added on to the end of February, the shortest month of the year. In regular years, February has 28 days, but in Leap Years it has 29.

Why is this special year called Leap Year? Because when you add February 29 to the calendar, it appears where March 1 normally is. What happens to March 1? It skips, or "leaps over," that day. It now appears on the calendar where March 2 normally is. March 2 then "leaps over" its normal place to where March 3 usually is, and so on.

The purpose of Leap Year is to keep the calendar in step with the seasons. The calendar is a kind of clock for the entire year. But how long is a year? A calendar year is 365 days. However, a true year is actually 365 days, 5 hours, 48 minutes, and 46 seconds long. That's the time it takes the Earth to travel around the sun, and it's called a solar year. We make up for the extra 5 hours, 48 minutes, and 46 seconds by adding one day to the calendar every four years.

The next Leap Year will be the year 2000. What a great way to start the 21st century!

Happy Birthday to Me

The chance of being born on February 29 in a Leap Year is 1 in 1,461. What would *you* do if you were a "29er"? You probably wouldn't like to celebrate your birthday only once every four years. So you would do what all 29ers do—you would celebrate your birthday on February 28 or March 1.

SUITS OF ARMOR

Would you like to make your very own suit of armor to wear on Halloween? You can, but first you must decide if it will be a suit of animal armor—like a turtle's protective shell. Or will it be a suit of metal armor—like the armor worn by knights on the battlefield long ago.

What You Need to Make Turtle Armor:

Decorations
Paints
Paintbrush
2 Fruit Trays
Felt
Ribbon
Glue

1. Paint and decorate two trays to look like the top and bottom of a turtle's shell.

2. Make felt straps to go over your shoulders. Glue them to the top of the inside of each tray.

3. Poke holes in the sides of the trays. Tie two pieces of ribbon through them, front to back.

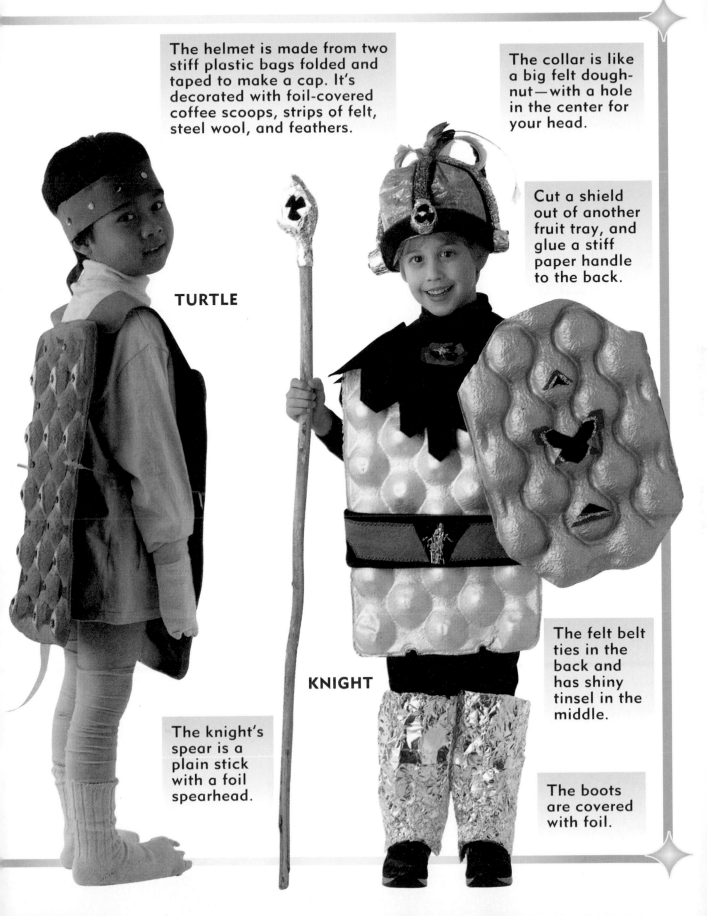

The helmet is made from two stiff plastic bags folded and taped to make a cap. It's decorated with foil-covered coffee scoops, strips of felt, steel wool, and feathers.

The collar is like a big felt doughnut—with a hole in the center for your head.

Cut a shield out of another fruit tray, and glue a stiff paper handle to the back.

TURTLE

KNIGHT

The knight's spear is a plain stick with a foil spearhead.

The felt belt ties in the back and has shiny tinsel in the middle.

The boots are covered with foil.

THE THUNDERBOLT SHOW

Thunderbolt raced across the television screen with Dirty Dawson just inches behind him. "I'll get you, you varmint!" Dawson snarled, swinging a heavy net as if it were a lasso.

"Run, Thunderbolt!" called Lucky as he watched in the living room of the Dalmatian Plantation. "You can beat that lily-livered, goose-gizzard Dirty Dawson rotter!"

"Why, Lucky! What kind of language is that?" Perdita shut off the television.

"Dirty Dawson always talks like that," Lucky told his mother.

"Then I think it's time for you to stop listening to Dirty
Dawson," Perdita told him. "I want you to go outside and play.
That's much better than watching TV."

"But—"

"Now, Lucky," Perdita said firmly.

Lucky walked slowly out to the backyard. It was so boring
out there. There was never anything to do. He lay down,
feeling sorry for himself, and put his chin on his paws. But
suddenly he brightened up, as he spotted a big brown box
waiting for the rubbish man. Its front was cut out, and to
Lucky, it looked just like a TV! Patch was napping inside, but
other than that, the box was perfect. If I can't watch television,
Lucky thought, maybe I can *play* it!

"Wake up, Patch!" Lucky said. "We're going to put on the
Thunderbolt show right here."

"Huh?" said sleepy Patch.

"Let's see. . .Rolly can do the Kanine Krunchies commercial, and Penny can be the announcer," Lucky continued.

Patch was wide awake now. "Who do I get to be?"

"Dirty Dawson."

Patch wrinkled his nose. "Why do I have to be the bad guy?"

"Because you already have the black eye," Lucky explained.

Rolly and Penny came up, and Lucky told them what their roles would be. "And soon," he added, as he left to find a costume for himself, "Thunderbolt himself will be here!" Since the show was his idea, Lucky decided that he would play Thunderbolt.

"Thunderbolt!" Rolly and Penny wagged their tails. "Here? That's what he said, isn't it, Patch?"

"He said they're going to put on the Thunderbolt show right here!" Patch nodded. "We should practice our—"

"We should go and tell everyone!" Rolly and Penny ran off to tell the beagle family who lived across the field. Penny raced off to tell the dachshunds who lived down the road. Patch hurried to tell all his other sisters and brothers. Soon, all the puppies were telling their friends. By the time Lucky came back to the box with a magazine photo he meant to use as a Thunderbolt mask, the backyard was filled with hundreds of pups and dogs, yapping excitedly. They got even more excited when Lucky stepped into the box to announce the show.

It took a minute before Lucky could make out their words. "Thunderbolt's coming!" "A real star in our own backyard!"

"Lucky's so clever to invite him!" And from Rolly, "Do you think he'll bring Kanine Krunchies?"

Then the dogs began flooding Lucky with questions. "When will he be here, Lucky? Where's Thunderbolt?"

"Wait a minute," Lucky said weakly, and he ducked behind the box and dropped the picture he was carrying. What was he

going to do? He couldn't go out there in disguise. Everyone would know it wasn't the real Thunderbolt. The yapping and barking were getting so loud that Lucky couldn't even think of a plan.

Suddenly a commanding bark rose above the noise. Lucky peeked around the box just in time to see a sleek chauffeured

limousine pull to a stop in front of their house. Leaning out of
the back window was the real Thunderbolt!

"Hello, youngsters!" Thunderbolt barked. As the chauffeur
got out of the car, Thunderbolt let himself out through the

window. The mob of puppies
and dogs raced over to him.
Lucky slipped out from behind
the box, but hung back when he
saw his parents coming out of
the house. He would be in for it
now!

But Lucky heard his father
say, "Well, hello, Thunderbolt.
This is quite a surprise." Pongo

looked around at the puppies and dogs. "Although your fan club certainly seems to be here."

Thunderbolt nodded. "It's a surprise for me, too. My pet and I were returning from the location where we were shooting an episode. I'm afraid my pet lost his way. When we saw the crowd here, I knew we would find help."

"Oh, yes, our pets will help," Perdita said. "They're very kind."

Thunderbolt smiled as Roger and Anita came out of the house to talk to his pet. "Actually, when I saw all the Dalmatians, I realized this must be the home of the famous Pongos. All of dogdom knows you. We were so pleased when you recovered the pups. I was about to set out on a search myself when I heard you had found them."

"How thoughtful," said Perdita.

Just then, Lucky found the courage to talk to Thunderbolt. After all, he had promised the others a Thunderbolt show. "Would you show us some of your tricks, Thunderbolt?"

Pongo smiled. "This is my son, Lucky. He's your biggest fan."

Perdita nudged Lucky playfully. "But the way he sometimes talks, I think he's a Dirty Dawson fan, too."

Thunderbolt bowed. "I would be delighted to perform for the Pongos." He turned to Lucky. "All right, son, you can be Dirty Dawson. But don't speak the way he does. No dog wants to sound like that."

Lucky nodded seriously, and Perdita smiled.

"Ready?" Thunderbolt called to Lucky. Then, in a flash, Thunderbolt streaked across the backyard with Lucky close

behind. Without warning, Thunderbolt stopped in his tracks, turned, and soared through the air right over Lucky's head.

"That's my fast getaway," Thunderbolt told them.

The puppies and the dogs barked their approval as Thunderbolt raced around in circles. Then, all of sudden, he disappeared. The dogs and puppies looked around, astonished. Just as suddenly, Thunderbolt leaped from behind the box, surprising them all. "When a boulder's not handy," he said, "I'll take any hiding place I can. The trick is to be so quick that Dirty Dawson can't tell where I've gone."

Thunderbolt's pet came out of the house with the Dalmatians' pets. "I'm afraid I must go," said Thunderbolt. "It was a pleasure meeting you youngsters. And a privilege to meet your brave parents. The next time we're here on location, you must come to see me."

But before Thunderbolt left, he posed for pictures that Roger and Anita took. "This gives me an idea for a song, Anita," Roger said.

Pongo, Perdita, and all the Dalmatian puppies and their friends barked and yapped their thanks to Thunderbolt.

Perdita watched Thunderbolt climb into the car, then lean out the window to give one final farewell bark. "He is quite a gentledog, isn't he, dear?" Perdita said.

"Yes, he is," Pongo nodded heartily.

"Perhaps it's not so bad for the children to watch his show," she added.

"I think you're right, Perdy," Pongo agreed.

The puppies barked their agreement, too. Lucky was still watching the car drive off. "You know, Mother, you were right about other things, too. I shouldn't talk like Dirty Dawson." Then he grinned. "And playing outside was much better than watching TV!"

Perdy nodded. "Yes, dear. I think we all learned something today."

"I learned that Lucky puts on the best shows ever," said Patch. "What will you do next, Lucky?" he asked as his brother went over to the box.

But Lucky was already fast asleep, dreaming about his next adventure with Thunderbolt.

The fangs of this ocelot, or leopard cat, are deadly weapons.
They are used to catch birds and other small creatures.

#

Animals have an amazing number of weapons to fight off enemies and capture food. They use teeth to bite, horns and antlers to batter, claws to scratch, and quills and spines to stab. Some poison their enemies or spray them with a powerful gas. And a few can "shoot" their next meal with long sticky tongues or a stream of water bullets.

Sharp teeth, along with strong jaws, are the weapons of wild cats and other hunting animals. They use their fangs—two long, pointed teeth in the upper jaw and two in the lower—like daggers. Animals such as elephants and walruses are armed with tusks—extra-long teeth that grow out of an animal's mouth.

While some weapons grow out of animals' mouths, others grow out of their heads. Goats, sheep, cattle, antelopes, and other grazing animals have horns on their heads. Some are short and curved, and others are long and sharp like swords.

Male moose fight with their antlers to see who will mate with a female. They also use their antlers to fight off enemies.

But the biggest "head" weapons are the antlers of many members of the deer family. The antlers of some male moose are 6 feet across!

Claws are another important animal weapon. Lions, tigers, and all other cats use their claws to hook their prey. Except for the cheetah, all cats can pull their claws back into their toes. When a cat runs or walks, it keeps its claws pulled in so they will not be blunted by the hard ground. When it climbs or fights, it pushes its claws out.

This grizzly cub will learn to use its sharp claws to fight off enemies.

Other animals with claws—such as bears, dogs, and raccoons—cannot pull their claws in. These animals use their claws mainly for digging or climbing rather than hunting or fighting. Even so, when a bear strikes an enemy with its powerful front paws, its long, curved claws can rip and tear and kill a large animal.

Quills and spines are other effective animal weapons. The little porcupine is the best-known quilled animal. When it swats an enemy with its tail, it drives hundreds of quills into it.

These long stiff hairs, tipped with tiny barbs, are pulled out of the porcupine and stay buried in the enemy's body.

The spines of a porcupine fish are like the prickly thorns of a rose bush. Usually, a porcupine fish swims about with its spines lying flat against its body. But when alarmed, it gulps water and air and swells up like a prickly balloon. Its spines stick out in all directions, ready to stab an enemy.

Many animals use poison as a weapon. These include hornets, bees, wasps, snakes, spiders, and fish. One such fish is the stonefish that lives in the waters

The quills of a porcupine (left) and the spines of a porcupine fish (below) are powerful animal weapons. Most enemies steer clear of these prickly creatures.

off Australia. Covered with warts, it is one of the ugliest fish in the world. It is also the deadliest. The jagged spines that stick out from its body contain a powerful poison that can quickly kill an enemy.

Some animals are armed with a bad-smelling chemical spray. The skunk is the champion mammal "stinker." And the bombardier beetle is one of the champion insect "stinkers." It bombs its enemies with a hot, smelly gas that shoots out from the tail end of its body.

The African chameleon keeps its weapon holstered—in its mouth. But when it spots an insect or small reptile, it takes aim, opens its mouth,

The ugly little stonefish (above) has 18 jagged and poisonous spines on its body. The bombardier beetle (right) defends itself by spraying enemies with an irritating gas.

Sharpshooters of the animal world include the African chameleon (above) and the archerfish (right).

and fires. Its long tongue, with its sticky tip, shoots out and grabs the meal.

Another "shooter" is the archerfish of Australia and Southeast Asia. This strange fish waits just below the surface of a pond, with its mouth sticking out of the water. When it spots an insect or spider on a leaf, the archerfish knocks it into the water by shooting a stream of water bullets at it. Then the fish gobbles up its meal.

THE JOKE'S ON YOU!

What's black and white and black and white and black and white?

A penguin in a revolving door!

Why did the farmer use a steamroller in his field?

Because he wanted to grow mashed potatoes!

How do you catch a rabbit?

Hide behind a bush and make a noise like a carrot!

What did one arithmetic book say to the other?

I really have a lot of problems!

What did the beaver say to the tree?

It's been nice gnawing you!

Why did the puppies sleep so close to the stove?

They wanted to be hot dogs!